EDGE

NO. 6

TABLE OF CONTENTS

MYSTIC
Chapters 23 & 24

Sometimes even magical protectors just want to have fun.

WAY OF THE RAT
Chapter 2

The Silken Ghost gives Boon mere hours to recover an ancient artifact.

RUSE
Chapter 9

Lightbourne resurfaces to make more trouble for Simon Archard.

THE FIRST
Chapter 19

Ingra finds herself in the many hands of Ervulsh.

SIGIL
Chapters 24 & 25

Sam and Zanni are reunited amidst the smoking rubble of Gaia.

SCION
Chapters 25 & 26

Ethan and Bron head toward a final confrontation!

www.comicsontheweb.com

MYSTIC™

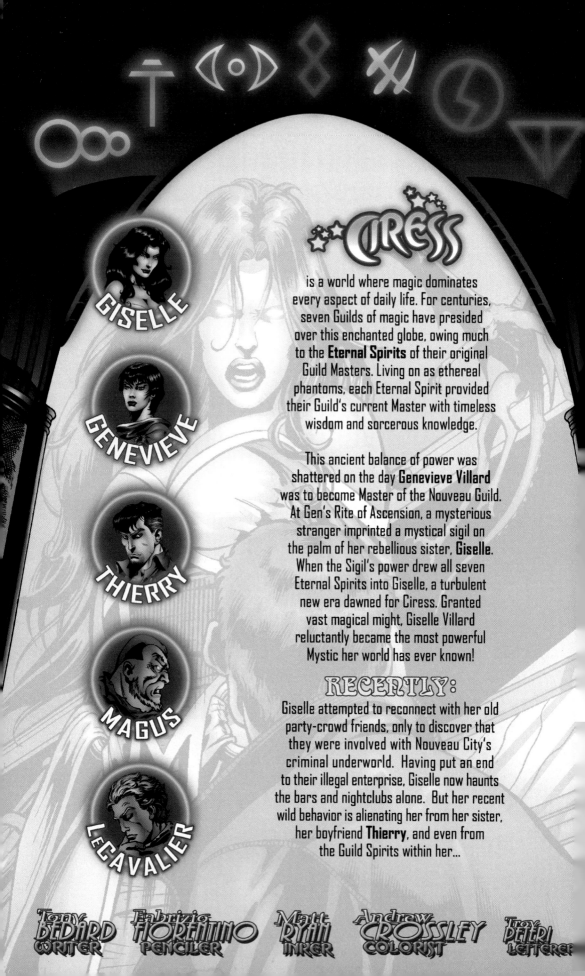

CHAPTER 23

CIRESS

is a world where magic dominates every aspect of daily life. For centuries, seven Guilds of magic have presided over this enchanted globe, owing much to the **Eternal Spirits** of their original Guild Masters. Living on as ethereal phantoms, each Eternal Spirit provided their Guild's current Master with timeless wisdom and sorcerous knowledge.

This ancient balance of power was shattered on the day **Genevieve Villard** was to become Master of the Nouveau Guild. At Gen's Rite of Ascension, a mysterious stranger imprinted a mystical sigil on the palm of her rebellious sister, **Giselle**. When the Sigil's power drew all seven Eternal Spirits into Giselle, a turbulent new era dawned for Ciress. Granted vast magical might, Giselle Villard reluctantly became the most powerful Mystic her world has ever known!

RECENTLY:

Giselle attempted to reconnect with her old party-crowd friends, only to discover that they were involved with Nouveau City's criminal underworld. Having put an end to their illegal enterprise, Giselle now haunts the bars and nightclubs alone. But her recent wild behavior is alienating her from her sister, her boyfriend **Thierry**, and even from the Guild Spirits within her...

GISELLE

GENEVIEVE

THIERRY

MAGUS

LECAVALIER

Tony BEDARD
WRITER

Fabrizio FIORENTINO
PENCILER

Matt RYAN
INKER

Andrew CROSSLEY
COLORIST

Troy PETERI
LETTERER

GISELLE, WHAT'S GOING ON? ARE YOU TRYING TO GET *ARRESTED*?

THERE WERE A FEW RUDE GUYS HERE, THAT'S ALL.

WHAT HAPPENED TO YOUR *BUDDIES*? LORRAINE, ANNETTE... *THOSE* GUYS?

DIDN'T YOU HEAR? TURNS OUT THEY'VE BEEN DEALING *PIXIE DUST*.

NOT THE RIGHT SET FOR A GIRL TO BE *SEEN* WITH--LEAST OF ALL THE GUILD MASTER'S SISTER. RIGHT, GEN?

GISELLE, I'M SORRY ABOUT YOUR FRIENDS. BUT THIS KIND OF BEHAVIOR ISN'T MUCH BETTER. I REALLY THINK YOU SHOULD--

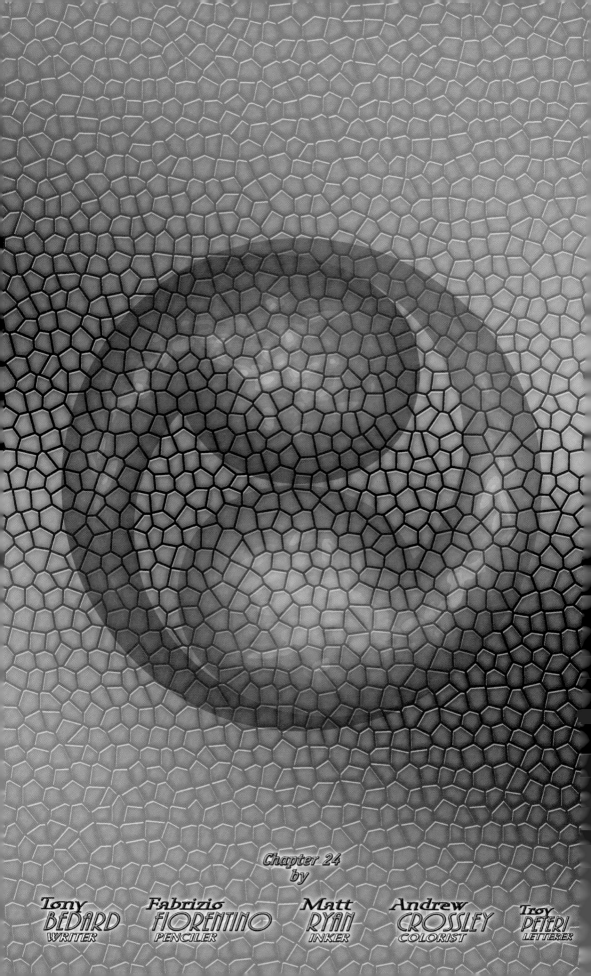

Chapter 24
by

Tony
BEDARD
WRITER

Fabrizio
FIORENTINO
PENCILER

Matt
RYAN
INKER

Andrew
CROSSLEY
COLORIST

Troy
PETERI
LETTERER

I'M FINALLY GOING TO *RIP* THAT SMUG SMILE OFF YOUR *FACE!*

YOU DON'T EVEN REALIZE WHAT YOU'RE UP AGAINST! YOU'RE ABOUT TO *LEARN* WHAT THE SIGIL CAN DO TO ONE OF *THE FIRST!*

BY ALL MEANS, *SHOW ME.*

ALL THE POWER IN THE *UNIVERSE* CAN'T SAVE YOU NOW! IN FACT, THE STRONGER *YOU* ARE, THE STRONGER YOU'LL MAKE *ME!*

FWASH

≈NNF≈...YES...THIS IS THE PART WHERE I'M SUPPOSED TO *WITHER* AS YOU DRAIN THE STRENGTH FROM MY LIMBS, RIGHT?

WHAT--? WHY AREN'T YOU...?

YOU'VE BEEN IN EXILE TOO LONG, ANIMORA, ELSE YOU'D *KNOW* THAT A SIGIL-BEARER RECENTLY CAME TO FAIR ELYSIA.

WATCHING HIM STEAL POWER FROM OTHERS REMINDED ME OF HOW *WE* GRANT ENERGY TO MORTAL *UNDERLINGS.*

BUT HAVE YOU EVER *RESCINDED* POWER FROM A PARTICULARLY *WILLFUL* UNDERLING?

FIZZLE

Oh. AND I SUPPOSE YOU WANT ME TO TAKE CARE OF THIS "THREAT" FOR YOU...?

HA! I REQUIRE NOTHING FROM YOU.

I HAVE LESS INTEREST IN BEING YOUR NEXT MASTER THAN YOU WOULD IN EMPLOYING A MOSQUITO.

NO, I HAVE DIVERSION ENOUGH RIGHT HERE.

AND I DOUBT YOUR WORLD WOULD FARE TOO WELL WERE I TO COME THERE AND HANDLE THE PROBLEM MYSELF.

I MERELY HOPE MY WARNING WILL SPUR YOU TO FINALLY TAKE POSSESSION OF YOURSELF.

THERE IS NOTHING SADDER THAN SQUANDERED POTENTIAL.

THE CHOICE IS YOURS, GISELLE VILLARD. I TRUST YOU'LL VINDICATE MY FAITH IN YOU.

NOW IT'S TIME FOR YOU TO GO HOME.

PERHAPS WE SHALL MEET AGAIN UNDER MORE PLEASANT CIRCUMSTANCES.

WAIT A MINUTE...

CHAPTER 2

The years of peace are at an end for the August Empire. From within, dark forces threaten the serenity of the Imperial City. From without, enemies from the steppes gather beyond the walls of civilization.

In these turbulent times, lost amidst events far larger than himself, lives a common thief of uncertain parentage named Boon Sai Hong. His home is the city of Zhumar, a walled fortress on the Empire's frontier.

The story of this humblest of lives would be as a single grain lost in a sandstorm but for a series of events that lead Boon to the possession of ancient objects with the power to change the world.

Boon has now seen but a glimpse of the significance of these mystic objects and wishes to deny destiny's claim upon him.

But the monkey has other ideas...

Chuck **DIXON** WRITER

Jeff **JOHNSON** PENCILER

Tom **RYDER** INKER

Chris **GARCIA** COLORIST

Dave **LANPHEAR** LETTERER

≈UNNH!

THE ANCIENT BOOKS OF DAYS TO COME *TOLD* OF ONE BORN IN THE YEAR OF THE RAT.

THIS WORTHY ONE WOULD TAKE POSSESSION OF *THREE* OBJECTS OF CELESTIAL POWER.

A RING. A BOOK. THE HEART OF THE PHOENIX.

I *HAVE* THE CURSED BOOK.

AND I CAN'T GET THE *RING* OFF MY HAND.

BUT I *DON'T* HAVE THE PHOENIX HEART.

YOU DON'T *HAVE* IT?

NO!

THEN WHO *DOES?*

CHAPTER 9

The PENNY ARCADIAN

Copiously Illustrated   Afternoon Edition, Price One Penny

CRIME RATE PLUMMETS

OUR PLAYERS

SIMON ARCHARD

THE CITY'S FAVORITE SON, HIS MIND IS RAZOR-SHARP

EMMA BISHOP

A FETCHING BEAUTY, HER SPIRIT CRAVES ADVENTURE

MALCOLM LIGHTBOURNE

A CUNNING CRIMESMITH
WITH COUNTENANCE UNREVEALED

ARCHARD SETS THE PACE

BLUDGERS AND HOODLUMS QUAKE FEARFULLY

Following a brief excursion to the East Country, detective Simon Archard returned last week to his Partington headquarters freshly spirited. Attacking with vigor every crime committed and mystery unveiled in his absence, within hours Archard had recovered the Merriwell jewelry collection, brought to justice the perpetrator of the Humbert murder, and solved the incomprehensible Riddle of the Turnabout Crypt.

With stamina undaunted, Archard then set to the task of gathering evidence against the long-ensconced Worthers Mob, foulest scourge of the city. Working tirelessly for some thirty-six hours with no respite, Archard shattered the network of this nefarious crime syndicate without so much as leaving his armchair, sending the mob deep into seclusion.

Close observers, however, are baffled that Archard's newfound intensity and groundbreaking detections seem wholly unrelated to the reappearance of Archard's former partner, Malcolm Lightbourne. All available information suggests that Lightbourne, having escaped

"NO REST FOR THE WICKED, CLAIMS DETECTIVE SIMON ARCHARD

pursuit following the attempte murder of Archard's assistan Emma Bishop, is still at large an still a threat to the citizens of th city. While Archard's motive are, as always, known only t himself, it is with no sma curiosity as to why Partington favorite son has yet to focus h efforts on Lightbourne's captur

•••PLEASE CONTINUE INSI

As It May Please the Court and Barristers of Our Fine Land

Mark
WAID
WRITER

Butch
GUICE
PENCILER

Michael
PERKINS
INKER

Laura
DePUY
COLORIST

Dave
LANPHEAR
LETTERER

NOTHING.

ARRESTS
Extraordinary Scenes.

pursuing the brigands who Thurs-
...ved Eddowes Jewelry of the fa-
...Sapphire, detectives Malcolm
...imon Archard exposed the

thieves as none
ins of proprietor B...
clues left by the daring
edly deduced and evaluated by th...

...I.T. BOUTON MURDER
...OLVED

Wynne B...
working in...
District, was ap...
y Malcolm Light...
d Simon Archar...
l with the h...
f Alice...

...CATE...

OMAN
OCKINGLY
ISONED!

ng woman named Jane

sary... ...dicine.
and ... ...she
went o... ...some
sweets wi... ...te her
medicine. Trag... ...young
life was cut short by a dose of
poison inside...he sweets, an instrument of murder which was
intended for a Partington lawyer as part of an altogether sep-
...te crime. The detection
...cy of Lightbourne & Arch-
...d was the first to determine
...he truth behind Miss Beat-
...'s untimely death, and
...in such mat-

THE sensation of...
has been Saturday's...
by the *Lightbourne-*
Agency, of the unique...
of killing employed in...
strom Murder. Foun...
in a room locked fro...
side with only a pud...
ter at his feet, Norman...
strom, it was presumed, c...
not have found purcha...
close to the ceiling w...
some surface upon whi...
stand. However, no ch...
other object of th...

Yet another additi...
to the long...
avenged by the...
of Lightbourne...
Friday morni...
ten o'clock, ju...
decked itself...
lands for the...
a ...ing o...
a... ...a...

The horrible dens of vice and
crime that have so long
plagued our fair city have endured yet another upheaval at
the hands of Malcolm Lightbourne and Simon Archard.
Working with full governmen...
tal authority, th...
team t...

Great excitement was occasioned
this morning when it was reported
that detectives Malcolm Lightbourne and Simon Archard had
last exposed the secrets...
the Mystery of the S...
Their investiga...
light new...
Stath...
h...

RANGE
CURENC
BLUMJIN...

PARTINGTON
GRATEFUL!

...following...
...ouched for...

...skeleton astrid...
...f a ro... ...ale green mare. Inquiries
...ale green mare. Inquiries
...upon th...
...me-A...
...y res...

FOR WEEKS NOW, I'VE BEEN ATTEMPTING TO INVEIGLE FROM SIMON INFORMATION AS TO HIS PAST.

SPECIFICALLY, HIS PAST PARTNER--A MADMAN BY THE NAME OF MALCOLM LIGHTBOURNE, WHO WAS PRESUMED DEAD FOR MANY YEARS--

--A FALSE ASSUMPTION GIVEN THAT HE NEARLY DROWNED SIMON, SWUNG AT ME REPEATEDLY WITH AN AXE, AND IS CURRENTLY AT LARGE.

...SORTED, ONE WOULD HAVE TO ASSUME, BY COLOR.

THUS MY HUNT FOR ARTICLES REGARDING THE LIGHTBOURNE-ARCHARD TEAM IS MADDENINGLY RANDOM...

...THOUGH NEVER DULL.

THE INCONCE
EXPLAI

Lightbourne,
Solve Grisly
In A Bottle'

STILL, WHILE THERE'S MUCH WRITTEN ABOUT THEIR CASES, THERE'S NOTHING ON LIGHTBOURNE THE MAN.

PARTINGTON detectives yesterday found the body of numismatist Victor Q. Smythe, bizarrely encased in a corked

THANK YOU FOR YOUR ASSISTANCE ON THE HUMBERT MURDER.

SIMON! I DIDN'T HEAR YOU--

WAIT.

I WASN'T HELPING WITH THAT. I WAS HERE.

YOU DON'T SAY.

Ah. HOW CONVENIENTLY WE IGNORE THAT YOU'VE BEEN SO ON THE MOVE THAT YOUR PARTNER--

ASSISTANT.

--PARTNER CAN'T FIND YOU, MUCH LESS AID YOU.

SPEAKING OF FINDING... THOSE ARE THE MORGUE FILES, YES?

OBITUARIES BY THE HUNDRED. DO YOU REALLY KEEP A RECORD OF EVERY SINGLE DEATH IN PARTINGTON?

A TOOL OF THE TRADE. AND WE CAN ADD A NEW CLIPPING.

AS USUAL, HOWEVER, SIMON IS ABOUT AS *FORTHCOMING* AS A *NUN* AT A *ROULETTE WHEEL*.

WHICH IS WHY I'VE BEEN IN *HERE* FOR THREE DAYS. SIMON OWNS PROBABLY THE SINGLE GREATEST LIBRARY COLLECTION IN THE WORLD, AND AMONG ITS REFERENCE WORKS ARE DECADES' WORTH OF BOUND NEWSPAPER VOLUMES...

Mmmh.

BONES ARE *CREAKING,* I'VE BEEN AT THIS SO LONG. AND STILL NO--

...

OH-HO. WHAT'S THIS?

OH.

NE OF OUR *AGENTS* -- A STABLEBOY AT THE *OXFORD-COLLINS* TATE--JUST TELEPHONED TH SOME VERY MUNDANE *EPORTAGE* REGARDING AN *UNFORTUNATE* INCIDENT.

JOIN ME.

BUT IF IT'S THAT *MUNDANE,* THEN WHY--

VERY WELL.

WHY, INDEED?

WHY HAVE WE COMPLETELY ABANDONED THE HUNT FOR *LIGHTBOURNE?*

THE MANSION AND SURROUNDING ACREAGE BELONGING TO LIONEL OXFORD-COLLINS TOGETHER CONSTITUTE THE SINGLE LARGEST PRIVATELY-HELD AREA OF LAND IN PARTINGTON.

IT TAKES LONGER TO WALK AROUND THE SOUTH SIDE THAN IT DID TO HANSOM HERE FROM SIMON'S HEADQUARTERS.

QUITE THE **STROLL**. I WISH YOU'D WARNED ME TO PACK A **LUNCH**.

IT'S DIFFICULT TO DECIDE WHICH IS MORE MELLIFLUOUS TO THE EAR:

YOUR DRONING COMPLAINTS THAT I LEAVE YOU **BEHIND**, OR YOUR DRONING COMPLAINTS THAT I TAKE YOU **ALONG**.

YET I **DO** ADMIRE THE **SCENERY**.

...CONVEY MY **CONDOLENCES**, GIRLS. IF ONLY WE'D BEEN RIDING **WITH** HIM WHEN HE--

ARCHARD? WHAT ARE **YOU** DOING HERE?

WE'LL SEE.

AH. GARFIELD BIGGS. THE LAWYERLY STENCH GIVES HIM AWAY.

AN UNREPENTANT CHAUVINIST WHO CAN'T ABIDE SEEING A WOMAN UNCHAINED FROM HER STOVE. HE'S SOILED OUR PATH BEFORE.

WELL, YOU'RE NOT **WELCOME** HERE, GOOD SIR. THERE'S NO TAWDRY **CRIME** FOR YOU TO SCRUTINIZE, NO **BLOOD** IN WHICH TO BATHE YOUR **HANDS**.

THIS CAN'T BE **HAPPENING**. DOCTOR, **PLEASE**...!

I DID ALL I COULD FOR YOUR FATHER, GIRLS...

...BUT HE'S **GONE**.

FOR A MOMENT, I THOUGHT H[] COULD...

BUT NO. DAMNE[] TICKER JUS[] GAVE OUT.

YOU'RE NOT ALONE. THE *CHURCH OF THE DRYADINE*-- NOTED WORSHIPPERS OF NATURE AND FAUNA-- MAKES ITS HOME ON THE GROUNDS IMMEDIATELY ADJACENT.

THEY'VE COUNTED OXFORD-COLLINS AS A MEMBER OF THEIR FAITH FOR *YEARS*...YEARS IN WHICH, I'M TOLD, THEY'VE BEEN TRYING TO COAX THEIR WAY INTO THE MAN'S *WILL*.

THAT'S AN ODD THING TO BRING *UP*, SIMON.

ODD...BUT *TIMELY*.

Oh, MY.

HEART ATTACK? WERE THERE ANY *WITNE*--

--I MEAN-- WAS THERE ANYONE WITH HIM AT THE TIME?

ALL OF *US*. EVERY FEW MONTHS, LIONEL ASSEMBLED HIS FRIENDS AND FAMILY AND UNLEASHED THE HOUNDS FOR A *GARGOYLE HUNT*.

THE BLAST OF LIONEL'S BUGLE SCATTERED US THROUGH THE WOODS IN TWOS AND THREES ON A MERRY CHASE.

"YOU'D BE SURPRISED AT HOW *STRENUOUS* RIDING CAN BE. JUST BECAUSE THE *HORSE* DOES MOST OF THE WORK DOESN'T MEAN YOUR MUSCLES WON'T *ACHE* AFTERWARDS.

"POOR LIONEL.

AS BIGGS FINISHES HIS TALE, SOMEONE *NEW* SPEAKS, AND I CAN TELL JUST BY LOOKING AT HER THAT SHE'S A *POETIC SOUL.*

THE ILLS THAT FLESH IS HEIR TO...

FAREWELL, KIND SIR. MAY GOD'S SOIL BLESS AND KEEP YOU.

AND MAY THE LEAVES AND THE FERNS AND THE FLOWERS LONG IN STEM WATCH AND PROTECT YOU AS THE SEASONS COME AND GO.

AN *ANNOYINGLY* POETIC SOUL.

HOW *DARE* YOU LAY CLAIM TO WHAT'S *RIGHTFULLY OURS,* YOU FILTHY *HAG?*

THIS LAND IS TO BE SHARED WITH *BELIEVERS,* YOU INSOLENT *CHILD.*

IF YOU'RE GOING TO BICKER OVER *INHERITANCE,* CAN YOU AT LEAST GET THE POOR MAN INTO A *GRAVE* SO HE CAN *ROLL OVER* PROPERLY?

DE*LIGHT*FUL.

"THE EXERTION WAS TOO MUCH FOR HIM."

"BY THE TIME HE'D HIT THE GROUND, HE WAS ALREADY GREY AS THE *GRAVE,* EACH BREATH MORE SHALLOW THAN THE LAST."

"THOSE OF US CLOSEST TO HIM CARRIED HIM BACK TO THE HOUSE IMMEDIATELY... BUT *'IMMEDIATELY'* WASN'T FAST *ENOUGH.*"

YRONDYNE. GH PRIESTESS F THE DRYADINE SECT.

SHE DOESN'T EXACTLY REEK OF *SINCERITY.* AM I THE ONLY ONE WITH THAT IMPRESSION?

NO.

Oh, SAVE THE *CROCODILE TEARS,* YOU TREE-STROKING *FREAK.* THEY'RE A *WASTE.*

FATHER MAY HAVE BOUGHT INTO YOUR ARCANE CLAPTRAP. *WE,* ON THE OTHER HAND, WANT YOU AWAY FROM *HIM* AND OFF *OUR LAND. NOW.*

"YOUR" LAND. THE TINY *ACORNS* CLAIM TO KNOW HOW LEANED THE *OAK.* HOW *JOCUND.*

HAT OICE.

WHEN *I* DIE, I HOPE *MY* MOURNING PERIOD LASTS MORE THAN *NINE* SECONDS.

I KNOW THAT VOICE. I...

I DIDN'T KNOW THE CIRCUS WAS IN TOWN.

WE ROLLED THROUGH YESTERDAY. HELLO, SIMON.

EMMA, MEET *OPHELIA PRESSMONK,* OTTO'S *TWIN.*

TWIN *WHAT?*

Ah. YOU MUST BE *EMMA BISHOP.*

EVERY TIME OTTO AND I VISITED THE *SNAKES* AT THE *ZOO,* HE MENTIONED *YOU.*

YES, DARLING, OUR MERRY CARAVAN ONCE MORE TRUNDLES INTO *PARTINGTON.*

VASHTI SENDS HIS BEST, BY THE WAY.

AND YOU'RE WITH US NOW *BECAUSE...?*

SAME REASON AS *YESTERDAY.* TO *BARGAIN.*

ON BEHALF OF THE *CIRCUS,* I APPROACHED MR. OXFORD-COLLINS ABOUT OUR SETTING UP ON THE NORTH-EAST CORNER OF HIS *ESTATE*--

--ONLY TO HAVE HIS *"LOVING"* DAUGHTERS *REBUFF* ME.

AND WE SHALL *AGAIN.*

IF YOU'VE THE *RIGHT.*

RST FLOOR, UTH WING. MET THERE EQUENTLY. WHY?

YOU, YOU, AND YOU-- STAY WITH THE BODY UNTIL THE CORONER ARRIVES. THE REST OF YOU, FOLLOW *ME.*

TO *WHERE?*

SIMON?

SIMON?

AH, SIMON. SUCH A WAY WITH *PEOPLE* YOU HAVE...

IT OCCURS TO ME THAT, GIVEN ALL THE *SQUABBLING* ABOUT WHO INHERITS *WHAT*...

...AN EXAMINATION OF OXFORD-COLLINS' *LAST WILL AND TESTAMENT* MIGHT BE IN ORDER.

MR. BIGGS, CAN YOU VERIFY THAT THIS OFFICE IS WHERE HE WOULD HAVE KEPT SUCH AN IMPORTANT DOCUMENT?

YES.

THEN WE HAVE A *PROBLEM*.

EVIDENTLY, SOMEONE BEAT US *TO* IT.

ON FILE, YES.

SO WE *HOPE*.

TELEPHONE YOUR OFFICE IMMEDIATELY. ENQUIRE AS TO ITS SAFETY. TELL YOUR SECRETARY YOU WISH HER TO MAKE *CERTAIN* IT IS *IN HAND*.

WHAT A FINE TURN OF *EVENTS*. WHOEVER RANSACKED THE ROOM TURNED IT *UPSIDE-DOWN* IN SEARCH OF ITS SAFE.

WHO CAN ACCOUNT FOR THEIR WHERE-ABOUTS?

WHAT? IS ANYONE *HURT*?

MISS YRONDYNE, WHERE WERE YOU EARLIER THIS AFTER-NOON?

WHERE I AM EVERY DAY. ENGAGED IN PRIVATE *MEDITATION* AMIDST THE SYCAMORE GROVE NORTH OF THE *CHURCH*.

WHAT? BUT *WHY*?

ISN'T IT *OBVIOUS?* BIGGS, YOU MUST HAVE A *COPY* OF THE WILL.

MAKE HER *PROVE* IT. AND DON'T LOOK AT *US*.

WE WERE ON THE *HUNT*.

AND YET, OFF ON YOUR *OWN*. I DON'T RECALL *SEEING* THE GIRLS THROUGHOUT MOST OF IT. OF COURSE, THEY COULD SAY THE SAME ABOUT *ME*...

SIMON, MY OFFICE HAS BEEN VANDALIZED AS WELL. LIONEL'S FILES ARE *GONE*.

YOU WERE HIS LAWYER. DO YOU KNOW THE SPECIFIC *DETAILS* OF HIS WILL?

AS PER LIONEL'S REQUEST, *NO*. HE WAS A *VERY* PRIVATE MAN.

I *CAN*, NEVERTHELESS, STATE WITH SOME CERTAINTY THAT THE ESTATE *EN TOTO* WAS LEFT *EITHER* TO THE DRYADINE CHURCH *OR* TO HIS DAUGHTERS BESS AND MARY, BUT *NOT* BOTH.

THIS LAND HAS BEEN IN LIONEL'S FAMILY FOR THREE CENTURIES. HE WAS ALWAYS ADAMANT THAT HE'D NEVER SPLIT IT UP.

BUT WHO *PROPERLY* INHERITS IT BECOMES A MATTER FOR *PROBATE COURT* SHOULD THE CHURCH CHALLENGE THE *GIRLS*.

AND WHY *SHOULDN'T* IT? DO YOU WANT TO KNOW HOW *DISAPPOINTED* LIONEL WAS IN THESE *ESURIENT* LITTLE *HARRIDANS* HE SIRED?

HOW *CONVINCED* HE WAS THAT THEY'D *SELL* THIS LAND TO SOULLESS DEVELOPERS WITHOUT A *MOMENT'S REGRET* SHOULD THEY BE ALLOWED THE *OPPORTUNITY?*

PLAINLY, *THEY* TURNED THIS OFFICE UPSIDE-DOWN!

WHY? WE *KNEW* WHERE THE *SAFE* WAS, UNLIKE *YOU,* YOU *FATUOUS--*

MR. ARCHARD, *ARREST* THIS WOMAN! SHE'S *GUILTY! GUILTY!* TAKE HER *AWAY!*

IN THE *FIRST* PLACE, THAT ISN'T WHAT I *DO.*

AND IN THE *SECOND* PLACE...

...I'M NOT INTERESTED IN *ANY* ACTIVITY THAT REQUIRES ENDURING ANOTHER *INSTANT* WITH *ANYONE* IN THAT ROOM.

YOU TOOK THE WORDS RIGHT OUT OF MY *MOUTH,* DARLING.

WRETCHED CREATURES, THE *LOT* OF THEM.

...SAID THE *POT* OF THE *KETTLE...*

CONTAINER HUMOR FROM THE *BOTTLE BLONDE.* COLOR ME *UNAMUSED.*

SEND HER *ALONG,* SIMON. THAT WAY, YOU AND I CAN PUT OUR...*HEADS* TOGETHER.

ABOUT THE MISSING *WILL?*

WELL, THERE'S THAT, *TOO.* I, IN FACT, HAVE A *THEORY* OR TWO...

ARE YOU SURE?

IT'S *NOT* OPHELIA

ARE YOU SURE?

ARE YOU SURE?

IT'S *NOT* OPHELIA

ARE YOU SURE?

IT'S *NOT* OPHELIA.

FINE. I'D ASK *HOW* YOU KNOW HER, BUT YOU WOULDN'T TELL ME. I'D ASK IF YOU YET KNOW WHO STOLE THE *WILL*, BUT YOU WON'T TELL ME THAT, *EITHER*.

SIMON, ALL REPARTEE ASIDE, YOU'RE GROWING *MORE* SECRETIVE AND *LESS* TRUSTING. IT'S *NOT* MY IMAGINATION. WHAT'S COME *BETWEEN* US?

...

ALL RIGHT. IT GOES BACK TO OUR ESCAPE FROM THAT SINKING *CARGO SHIP*.

DURING THE *MIRANDA CROSS* CASE.

WHEN WE RETURNED *HERE*, I FOUND A SINGLE STRAND OF LONG BLACK *HAIR* INSIDE MY COAT--

--UNTOUCHED BY THE *WATER*.

CURIOUS, I MOUNTED IT ON A MICROSCOPE SLIDE.

BLACK HAIR. *MIRANDA*. BUT I CAN'T TELL SIMON SHE WAS THERE WITHOUT SAYING TOO MUCH.

WHY WOULD YOU ASK ME?

BECAUSE, DURING MY ABSENCE *FOLLOWING* THAT CASE--

*T*HAT WENT POORLY.

I SHOULDN'T HAVE LET MY TEMPER GET THE BETTER OF ME. I SHOULD HAVE BEEN *KINDER* WITH SIMON...

...BECAUSE HE'S NOT *HIMSELF*. I'VE FINALLY GUESSED THE TRUTH ABOUT WHY HE'S AVOIDING THE MORE *PRESSING* CASE AT HAND.

IT'S *UNFATHOMABLE*... IT'S IN EVERY WAY *UNLIKE* SIMON...BUT IT'S THE ONLY THEORY THAT MAKES *SENSE*.

HE WAS YOUR FIRST *PARTNER*, SIMON, AND I SUSPECT HE WAS QUITE THE *MENTOR*, AS WELL.

THAT EXPLAINS THE *COMPETITIVE STREAK* HE STIRS IN YOU.

HE KNOWS HOW TO *GOAD* YOU, HOW TO *MANIPULATE* YOU.

YOU, OF *ALL* PEOPLE, MUST FIND THAT *TERRIFYING*.

BUT YOU HAVE TO PUT THAT FEAR *ASIDE*, SIMON, AND I'LL *HELP* YOU HOWEVER I *CAN*. I *MEAN* IT. YOU DON'T--

HERE.

--YOU DON'T *HAVE* TO BE *AFRAID* OF--

--AN ABSENCE IN WHICH YOU WERE THE ONLY PERSON WITH ACCESS *TO* THIS LAB--

--THE HAIR WAS *DESTROYED*.

IS THERE SOMETHING YOU WISH TO *TELL* ME?

FAR MORE THAN IS *GOOD* FOR YOU.

YOU'RE *ACCUSING* ME OF--?

SIMON ARCHARD, I HAVE *NO IDEA* WHAT BECAME OF YOUR *PRECIOUS EVIDENCE*. ON THAT, YOU HAVE MY *WORD*.

I'LL BE *DOWNSTAIRS* WHILE YOU DECIDE HOW YOU WISH TO *APOLOGIZE*.

COME TO ANY NEW OBSERVATIONS ABOUT *LIGHTBOURNE*?

YES.

YOU'RE *AFRAID* OF HIM.

I *SAW* HOW YOU REACTED WHEN THE GYPSIES SPOKE OF HIM, SIMON.

AND I *REMEMBER* HOW EMOTIONAL YOU BECAME BEFORE *THAT*, WHEN LIGHTBOURNE FIRST *ATTACKED*.

...

GOOD LORD.

IT'S I WHO MUST APOLOGIZE. THIS...

THEN YOU GRASP ITS *SIGNIFICANCE*.

I'M *BEGINNING* TO. WHY DIDN'T YOU BRING THIS UP BEFORE?

I HAD TO FIGURE OUT THE *WHY* OF IT FIRST. AND NOW THAT I *HAVE*--

"--THE 'WHO' OF IT IS PAINFULLY *APPARENT*."

SO YOU SAY YOU KNOW WHO PINCHED LIONEL'S *WILL*, SIMON?

OF *COURSE* HE DOES! WHY *ELSE* ASSEMBLE THE *DRAMATIS PERSONAE* AT THE SCENE OF THE *CRIME*?

WHAT A FLAIR FOR *THEATRICS* YOU HAVE, MR. ARCHARD.

EXTRA POINTS FOR THE *THUNDERSTORM*.

THANK YOU. I FIND IT'S THOSE EXTRA *TOUCHES* THAT SET THE STAGE SO *BEAUTIFULLY* WHEN ONE DISCUSSES *MURDER*.

M-*MURDER?* BUT LIONEL WASN'T--

THAT'S *ABSURD!* DON'T KEEP US IN *SUSPENSE*, MAN! IF THE *THIEF* IS ALSO A *KILLER*--

PATIENCE, BIGGS. I REMIND YOU AGAIN, WHEN EMMA SPARKED DISCUSSION, NO ONE COULD PROVIDE HIMSELF A REASONABLE ALIBI FOR THE TIME OF THE THEFT.

THAT--

--WAS *MY* JOB. NOTE THE *WINDOW PANE* CRACKED DURING THE BURGLARY.

WHEN EMMA AND I FIRST ARRIVED, WE CIRCUMNAVIGATED THE SOUTH WING--THIS WING. AT WHICH TIME THE WINDOWS WERE IN *PERFECT REPAIR*.

THE BROKEN GLASS SET THE THEFT *DURING THE PERIOD WE WERE ALL OUT BACK TOGETHER*.

WELL *OBSERVED*, MR. ARCHARD... AND *THANK* YOU. AT LEAST THAT CLEARS US.

OF *WHAT?*

EXCUSE ME...?

HE MOST CERTAINLY *WAS*. THIS, I'VE KNOWN FROM THE *START*. AND HIS *HUNTSMAN'S BUGLE* WAS THE *WEAPON*.

A QUICK SWAB OF ITS MOUTHPIECE EVINCED A SLOW-ACTING NICOTINE-DERIVATIVE POISON--

--ITS EFFECTS INDISTINGUISHABLE FROM A COMMON *CORONARY*.

HOW PERFECTLY *GHASTLY!* WHO WOULD HAVE...?

ANY OF YOU, FRANKLY. I'M QUITE CONFIDENT THE BUGLE WASN'T HARD TO *GET* AT. MOREOVER, NO ONE OFFERS A CLEAR ALIBI FOR *ANYTHING*, AND WITH THE *INHERITANCE* AT STAKE, MOTIVES *ABOUND*... INCLUDING *YOURS*, BIGGS.

MINE? YOU'RE *MAD!* WHAT *POSSIBLE* REASON COULD *I* HAVE FOR MURDERING LIONEL?

YOU SAID IT *YOURSELF*. WITH THE WILL *MISSING*, THE OXFORD-COLLINS *DAUGHTERS* COULD SPEND *YEARS*...*EXPENSIVE* YEARS...IN COURT AS YOU DEFEND THEIR *CLAIM*.

I NEVER SAID THE MURDERER AND THE THIEF WERE ONE AND THE SAME. *BIGGS* DID. AND WE *ALL* KNOW HOW OFTEN A *LAWYER* SPEAKS THE TRUTH.

THE IDENTITY OF THE *KILLER* IS NO MYSTERY AT *ALL*. AS A MATTER OF *FACT*, I KNEW *PRECISELY* WHO WAS GUILTY THE MOMENT I WAS *NOTIFIED* OF OXFORD-COLLINS' *FATE*... BEFORE I EVEN LEFT MY *HEADQUARTERS*.

the PENNY ARCA[DE]

ly Illustrated

Afternoon Edition, Price Ha'

MacGRUDER KILLER FOU[ND]

VICTIM'S CHILDREN WERE MASTERMINDS

INSTRUMENT OF HIS DEATH

MEMORIES ARE *SHORT*. WHILE *SOMEONE* WOULD EVENTUALLY HAVE MADE THE CONNECTION, I RECALLED IT *INSTANTLY*... AS WAS THE MACABRE *INTENT* OF THE CRIME'S SECRET *ENGINEER*.

TWELVE YEARS AGO, PARTINGTON SAW A MURDER ALMOST *IDENTICAL*--RIGHT DOWN TO THE *VERY LAST DETAIL*.

I REMEMBER THIS *VIVIDLY*--

CITY SLEUTHS CLAIM REWARD

-- BECAUSE IT WAS THE *VERY FIRST* CASE THE *LIGHTBOURNE-ARCHARD* TEAM EVER SOLVED.

HE NEVER *TOLD* YOU THAT YOU WERE PAWNS IN A *LARGER SCHEME*, DID HE, GIRLS?

WE...WE DON'T KNOW WHAT YOU'RE *TALKING* ABOUT...!

MARY, *RUN!* *RUN!*

I'VE BEEN *MEANING* TO SPEAK TO YOU ABOUT THIS. DESPITE YOUR *MANY* BRILLIANT TALENTS, YOU *DO* HAVE *ONE* GLARING FLAW.

YOU'RE *CONVINCED* THAT THE ACCUSED WILL, IN THE FACE OF YOUR *GENIUS*, FALL AND *PROSTRATE* THEMSELVES AND BEG *FORGIVENESS.*

YOU *MIGHT* WISH TO TAKE INTO ACCOUNT, THAT, MORE OFTEN, THEY *FLEE.*

NOW WHO HAS ISSUES OF TRUST?

OPHELIA, TAKE THE *KEY* AND *MEET* US. THE MATTER OF WHICH WE SPOKE *BEFOREHAND?*

ATTENDED TO...

SPARE ME.

LIGHTBOURNE'S BEHIND IT *ALL*. HE SOUGHT YOU *OUT*-- CHARMING *STRANGER* WITH A *PLAN*, AWARE OF YOUR *GREED*.

HE *PROPOSED* THE MURDER AND INSTRUCTED YOU IN THE *MECHANICS*.

AFTERWARD, WHILE WE WERE GATHERED, *HE* STOLE THE *WILL*--

--PILLAGING THE ROOM, NO DOUBT, TO COVER THE FACT THAT YOU'D *TOLD* HIM EXACTLY WHERE IT *WAS*.

TOGETHER, YOU--

WHUNF

≥KAFF≤

"...AS THEY'LL SOON *LEARN*."

QUICKLY! TO THE *STABLES!* WE CAN MAKE OUR ESCAPE BY *HORSEBACK!*

"OH, TO *BE* THERE."

BESS, THE *DOORS*--!

I *SEE!* SHUT *UP* AND LET ME *THINK!*

≥GASP≤

NO! BESS, HE'S *COMING!* HE KNOWS WHERE WE *ARE!*

WERE. HE KNOWS WHERE WE *WERE*.

THIS *WAY!*

GOD, I CAN BARELY *SEE...*

I CAN SEE *ENOUGH!* UP *THERE!*

POLICE CLOSING IN. *DAMN* YOU, ARCHARD.

BESS, WHAT'LL WE *DO?* LIGHTBOURNE WILL *KILL* US IF WE'RE CAUGHT! HE'LL *KILL US!*

SHUT UP! GET TO THE *LAKE!*

WELL *PLAYED.*

CHESS WITH *HALFWITS.*

SO LIGHTBOURNE SET THIS WHOLE AFFAIR IN MOTION SIMPLY TO *TAUNT* YOU?

NO.

THERE'S MORE *TO THIS,* LADIES! *WHAT'S* LIGHTBOURNE HIDING ON THE ESTATE?

TELL ME!

WE'LL →SPPT SPUTT← WE'LL *NEVER--*

YOU SHUT UP, BESS! IT'S *OVER!*

AS--AS PART OF OUR *DEAL,* HE TOLD US TO KEEP THE *CIRCUS* PEOPLE AWAY AT *ALL COSTS--* BUT HE WOULDN'T SAY *WHY!*

HE PROMISED IF WE PLAYED *ALONG,* WE'D GET THE INHERITANCE *PLUS* PAYMENT FROM *HIM!* AND THAT'S *ALL WE KNOW-- I SWEAR!*

PROBABLY *SO.* IF ANYTHING *ELSE* COMES TO MIND, TELL IT TO THE *POLICE.*

"WHAT'S LIGHTBOURNE HIDING?" WHAT DO YOU MEAN BY *THAT?*

IT'S *OBVIOUS...*

...THOUGH I ADM OPHELIA'S *PRESEN* MADE IT *CLEARE* TO ME.

Oh! Oh, I SEE! THE SUMMER *ROWBOAT!*

EXACTLY.

I'M NOT SO *STUPID* AS TO LEAVE OURSELVES ONLY ONE *EXIT...!*

HOW LONG BEFORE THEY TAKE *NOTE?*

OF THE *HOLE* IN THE BOTTOM? I'D SAY JUST ABOUT *NOW...*

BESS, WE'RE *SINKING!*

SHUT *UP!* SHUT UP, SHUT UP, *SHUT UP!*

ONE FRESH STEED, BRIDLED AS *ORDERED.* THERE'S ROOM FOR ONE AND A *HALF...*

NO THANK YOU, OPHELIA. I'LL RIDE *ALONE.*

OPHELIA'S *CIRCUSFOLK* WISHED ACCESS TO THE PROPERTY'S *NORTHEAST CORNER.*

LIGHTBOURNE HAD THE SISTERS CHASE THEM AWAY FOR THE SAME REASON HE MUDDLED THE LAND'S OWNERSHIP BY STEALING THE *WILL* --

--BECAUSE THERE'S SOMETHING *HERE,* LIKELY IN THE NORTH-EAST CORNER, HE WISHES TO ENSURE NO ONE *FINDS!* BUT *WHAT?*

I'LL KNOW *SOON.* THERE ARE *CAVES* THERE. I HAVE MY *SUSPICIONS.*

HYAH!

SIMON, *WAIT!*

WASTED WORDS. HE WAS ALREADY *GONE.*

I'D BEEN PROFOUNDLY MISTAKEN.

SIMON HADN'T BEEN IGNORING LIGHTBOURNE AT *ALL*. FAR *FROM* IT.

IT'S BEEN ABOUT LIGHTBOURNE *ALL* ALONG.

SIMON KNEW FROM THE START THAT THE TWO OF THEM WERE ENMESHED IN A MORBID AND JEOPARDOUS *GAME*...

...AND THAT *LIGHTBOURNE* DETERMINED THE *PLAYING FIELD.*

IN THE BEGINNING...

They were the gods who created the universe before descending into a constant state of war. Then their home, Elysia, was torn by the Eidolon rift as Altwaal separated the First into two Houses to end the warfare. Peace and boredom followed. Now the First have been catalyzed into action with the appearance of the Sigil-Bearers, beings of great power that was *not* given to them by the First, one of whom killed one of the First. If these Sigil-Bearers can destroy the First...their godhood itself is in question.

HOUSE SINISTER

HOUSE DEXTER

Pyrem, held prisoner in Braag's keep in House Sinister, is rescued by **Trenin** and **Yala**, but at the cost of the young Secundae Gracos' life. The conspirators behind Pyrem's kidnapping, **Seahn** and **Braag**, fight to keep their prisoner. Seahn faces off against Trenin, whom Seahn believes is his father, a fact that Trenin vehemently denies. Enson interferes, sending Seahn away. Ingra secretly helps with Pyrem's escape, an act witnessed by Braag, who goads her into an overwhelming display of strength that strips away the last of her power reserves — she teleports the entire Dexter contingent home, leaving her vulnerable to a combined attack by Seahn, Braag, Orium, and the enigmatic Enson. Meanwhile, Persha has gone to plead with Altwaal for his return. She finds Ayden, the man she believes to be Altwaal, on Quin. He doesn't admit to being Altwaal, but does send her on her way with the idea that perhaps *she* is the unifier she seeks.

Barbara
KESEL
WRITER

Andrea
DI VITO
PENCILER

Rob
HUNTER
INKER

Rob
SCHWAGER
COLORIST

Dave
LANPHEA
LETTERER

OUR STORY SO FAR...

SAM

ROIYA

JeMERIK

ZANNIATI

TCHLUSARUD

KHYRADON

FOR CENTURIES, the five human worlds of the Planetary Union have been at war with the lizardlike Saurians of Tcharun, unable to find a weapon formidable enough to turn the tide of battle. And then along came Sam.

A mustered-out soldier with a good heart, SAMANDAHL REY and his fellow ex-soldier ROIYA SINTOR came looking for work on the neutral world Tanipal only to be ambushed by Sam's Saurian enemy TCHLUSARUD. In the ensuing battle, they picked up two crucial allies – the mysterious JeMERIK MEER (smitten by Roiya) and ZANNI (a spy anxious to escape the harem of Tanipal's Sultan). Victory, though, came not from any of them but rather from a strange sigil, a brand of vast power burned into Sam's chest by a vanishing stranger. In fact, Sam first realized the sigil's potential when Roiya was slain – and Sam, in a moment of anguished grief, neutralized the attack by unintentionally unleashing a half-mile-wide explosion of matter-transforming force.

Once Sam, JeMerik and Zanni escaped Tanipal, however, an over-wrought Sam learned that all was not lost; while Roiya's lifeless body lay in stasis aboard Sam's starship, *the BitterLuck*, her mind and soul had been "uploaded" into the ship's computers seconds before her death, allowing Roiya to live on in holographic form. Now the two of them are taking point in defending the human race from the merciless Saurian army, with Sam on one side as the Planetary Union Field Commander and Khyradon, a self-styled war god, leading the Saurians in an all-out attack on the Union.

PREVIOUSLY...

Sam has prevented the full impact of the Saurian-launched asteroid from utterly destroying Gaia, but miles-wide chunks of the celestial object made planetfall and the death tolls are high and rising. Adding to his feeling of guilt is the knowledge that the sigil he bears has granted him powers beyond those he's utilized powers that might have revived Roiya and spared her from life a a mere holographic image.

On Tcharun, Tchlusarud, last son of the Matriarch, continues hi journey to the Saurian homeworld's northern hemisphere to begin lifelong banishment in the prison hell of Kholyma.

As our story resumes we find Sam reunited with Zanni after a long period of separation.

Chuck
DIXON
WRITER

Scot
EATON
PENCILER

Andrew
HENNESSY
INKER

Wil
QUINTANA
COLORIST

Dave
LANPHEAR
LETTERER

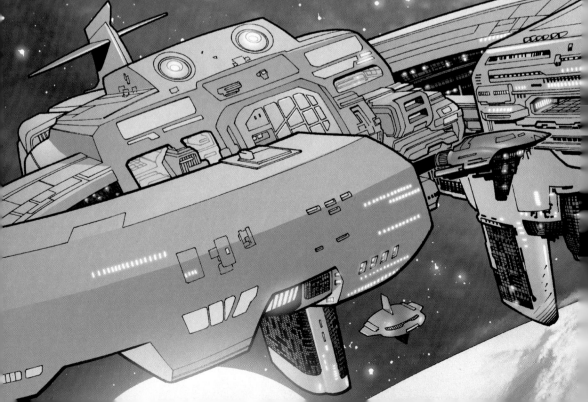

"IT'S *IMPOSSIBLE* TO COMPREHEND.

"ENTIRE SECTORS BURNED *CLEAN* OF LIFE.

"*HUNDREDS* OF MAJOR STRIKES ALL OVER THE WESTERN QUADS.

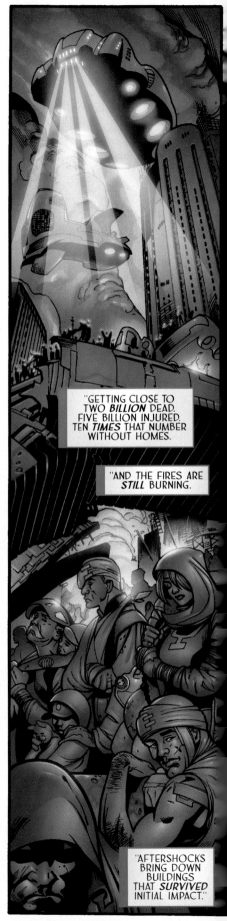

"GETTING CLOSE TO TWO *BILLION* DEAD. FIVE BILLION INJURED. TEN *TIMES* THAT NUMBER WITHOUT HOMES.

"AND THE FIRES ARE *STILL* BURNING.

"AFTERSHOCKS BRING DOWN BUILDINGS THAT *SURVIVED* INITIAL IMPACT."

SAMANDAHL REY?

YOU HAVE PEOPLE *TRAPPED* DOWN THERE?

UNDER MILLIONS OF TONS OF STEEL. IT'S A CHAOTIC JUMBLE.

MOVE THE WRONG BEARING BEAM AND--

I CAN TAKE THE LOAD OFF.

KEEP FEEDING ME *READINGS,* OKAY?

MORE TO YOU RIGHT.

WE NEED A *PATH* DOWN TO THEM.

NOT A *PROBLEM*

"EVERY AVAILABLE SHIP HAS BEEN ARMED AND ASSEMBLED IN GAIA'S ORBIT.

"THE NECESSARY DEFENSE SCREEN WILL BE MAINTAINED.

"ALL OTHER CRAFT WILL BE USED IN THE ASSAULT ON THE SAURIAN HOMEWORLD.

"THEY WILL LINK AT DELASSIA WITH OTHER OUT-SYSTEM PATROL FLEETS.

"OVER ONE THOUSAND SHIPS IN ALL.

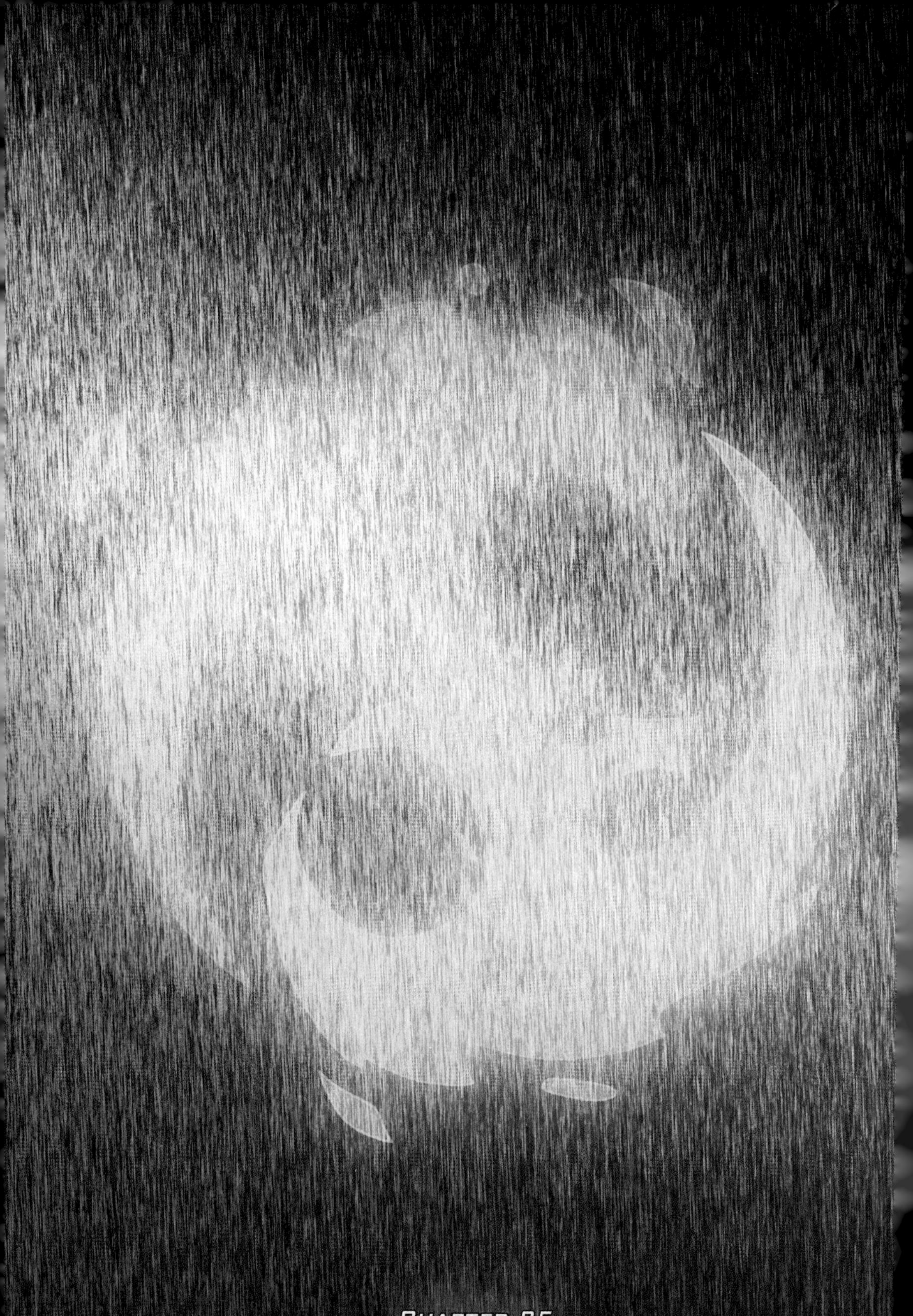

CHAPTER 25
BY

Chuck
DIXON
WRITER

Scot
EATON
PENCILER

Andrew
HENNESSEY
INKER

Wil
QUINTANA
COLORIST

Dave
LANPHEAR
LETTERER

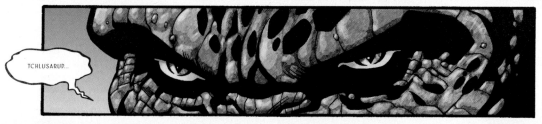

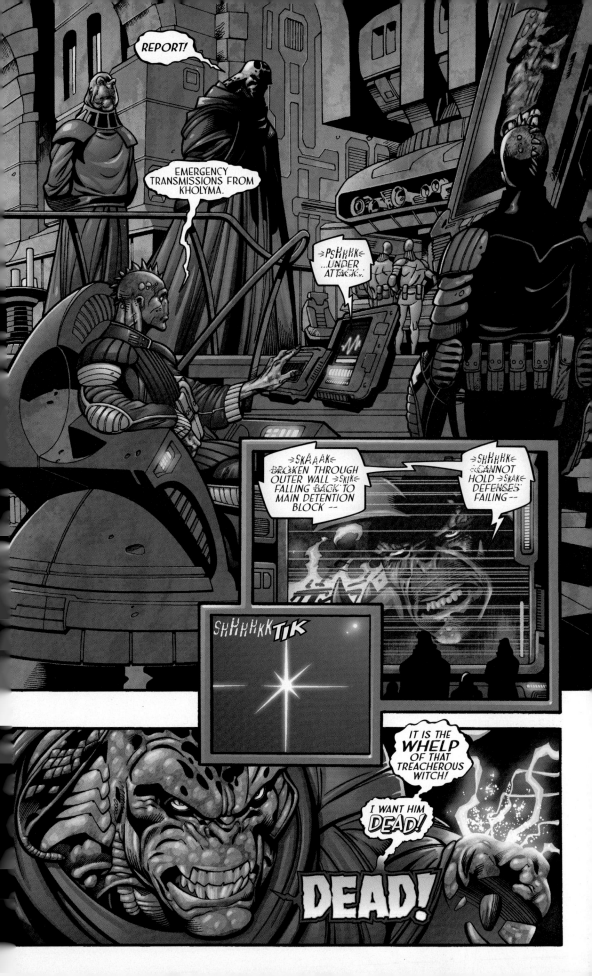

THE LAST OF THE GUARDS OFFER RESISTANCE.

WHAT *ORDERS*, TCHLUSARUD?

KILL!

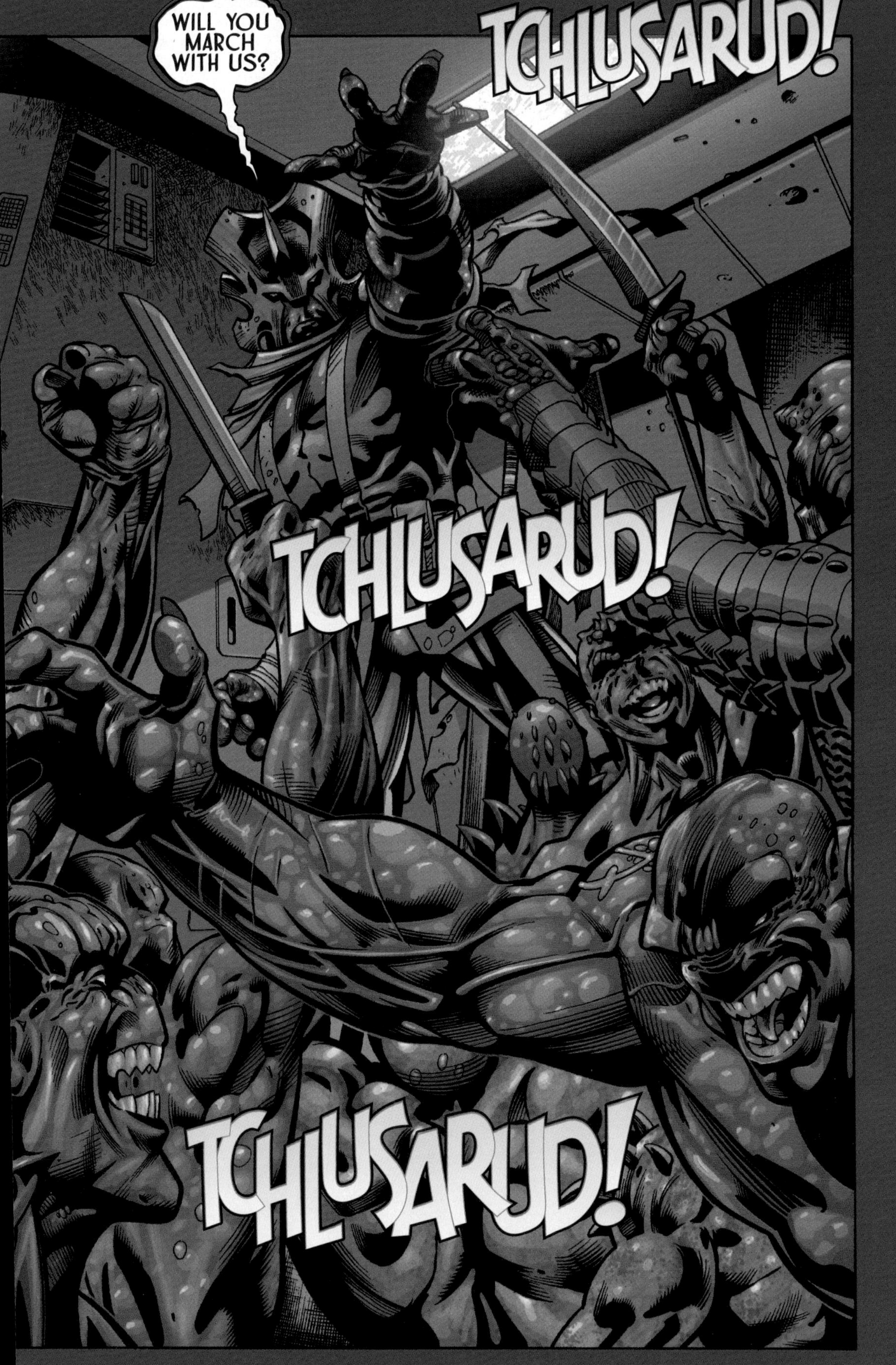
WILL YOU MARCH WITH US?
TCHLUSARUD!
TCHLUSARUD!
TCHLUSARUD!

CHAPTER 25

Thus Far in Scion

Ethan

Ashleigh

Skink

Bron

Mai Shen

Kai

Ylena

Dane

What started with a mysterious sigil led to war. Prince Ethan of the West-ruling Heron Dynasty was graced with a mark granting him power, leading to the accidental scarring of Prince Bron of the East-ruling Raven Dynasty during ritual combat.

When the battle was met, first victory belonged to the Herons, but Ethan's oldest brother and heir to the throne, Artor, was brutally slain by Bron. Ethan swore vengeance.

Not long after, Bron was imbued with power by Mai Shen, who revealed herself to him as a member of the godlike First. Bron then murdered his father, framed his sister Ashleigh for the crime, and took the throne for himself.

Ethan confronted Bron in the Raven Keep but was defeated, managing to escape with his life thanks to Ashleigh's help. The Raven princess was, in fact, part of the Underground movement dedicated to freeing the genetically engineered Lesser Races. Ethan promised his loyalty to the Underground, and he and Ashleigh eventually gave in to their mutual attraction.

Ethan and his companions successfully took the Tournament Isle, located in the Great Sea between Raven and Heron lands, as a sanctuary for the Lesser Races. When the fleets of both kingdoms converged on the Isle, Ethan used his power to end their conflict. Exhausted, Ethan washed ashore directly into Bron's hands.

Ron marz WRITER   **Jim cheung** PENCILER   **Don hillsman II** INKER   **Justin ponsor** COLORIST   **Troy peteri** LETTERER

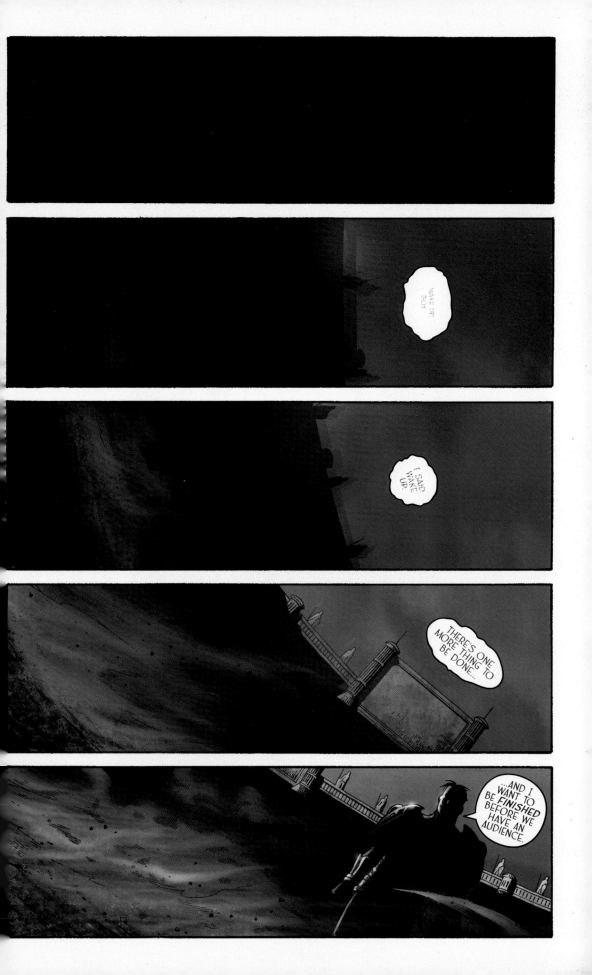

WHAT AM I DOING IN THE *ARENA?* HOW DID I *GET* HERE, BRON?

I *DRAGGED* YOU HERE AFTER YOU'D WASHED ASHORE.

ALMOST THE SAME PLACE *I* CAME ASHORE AFTER I WAS THROWN FROM MY SHIP.

PREVAILING CURRENTS, I SUPPOSE.

SO...

...A FITTING VENUE TO *END* THIS, DON'T YOU THINK? IT DID ALL *BEGIN* HERE.

YOU *IMPRESS* ME, ETHAN, SEPARATING THE FLEETS LIKE THAT.

SEEMS YOU EFFECTIVELY *ENDED* THE WAR.

AND TRUTHFULLY, I FIND I REALLY DON'T *CARE.*

MY ONLY CONCERN IS *KILLING* YOU.

YOU BEAT ME *ONCE*...

...BUT ONLY BECAUSE YOU WERE GRANTED *POWER.*

I'VE BEEN GIVEN THE *SAME* GIFT...

...AND YOU WON'T STAND AGAINST ME!

I'VE SEARCHED THE SHORELINE AROUND THE HARBOR AND BEYOND.

NO SIGN OF ETHAN.

I HAVE BURIED *ONE* SON, AND LIKELY HAVE LOST TWO *OTHER* CHILDREN.

I WILL NOT ACCEPT THAT ETHAN IS *GONE*...

...PARTICULARLY WHEN A *WITCH* OF RAVEN BLOOD IS TO BLAME.

ASHLEIGH IS NOT TO BLAME. SHE HAS BEEN ETHAN'S *SAVIOR*, AS WELL AS HIS LOVER.

HOW *DARE* YOU!

WHO ARE *YOU* TO SPEAK TO ME SO?!

I AM A FREE MAN IN A FREE LAND.

I HATE TO *DISAGREE* WITH YOU IN PUBLIC, FATHER...

WHAT'S THE MATTER, WHELP?

WHAT IS IT YOU *EXPECT*, BRON?

YOU WANT *ME* DEAD...

WHNF

I WILL SAY *THIS*— YOU'RE FINALLY GOING TO PAY THE *PRICE* FOR WHAT YOU DID TO MY BROTHER.

FOR WHAT YOU DID TO YOUR OWN *FATHER*.

THEN COME *COLLECT* IT.

NNG!

ETHAN *IS* HERE...

...AND SO IS *BRON!*

BUT... HOW CAN BRON EVEN BE *ALIVE?*

WE HAVE TO GET *DOWN THERE!* WE HAVE TO *HELP* ETHAN!

NO.

NO? SKINK, WHAT ARE YOU TALKING ABOUT? ETHAN *NEEDS* US!

THIS TEST HAS BEEN A LONG TIME IN COMING FOR ETHAN.

HE MUST FIGHT THIS BATTLE ALONE.

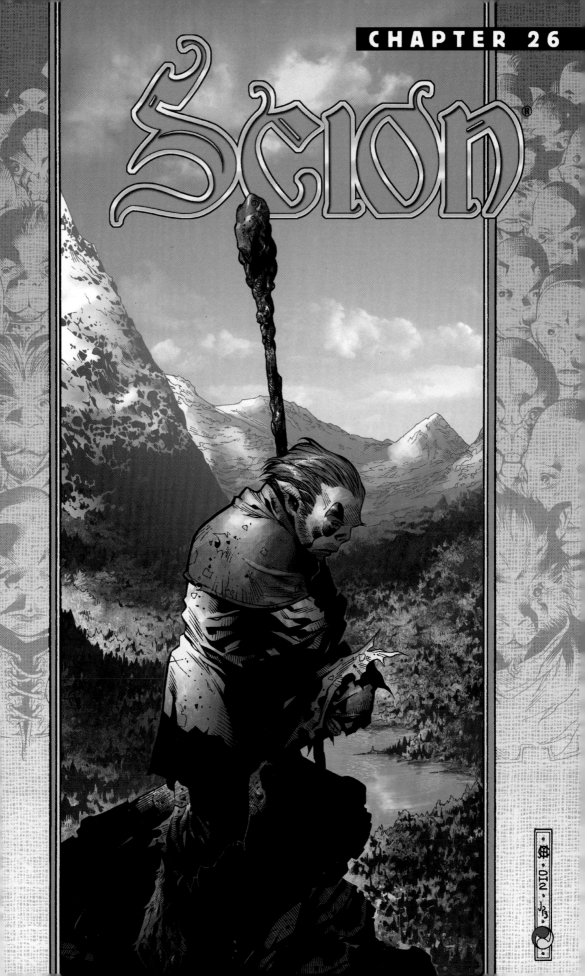

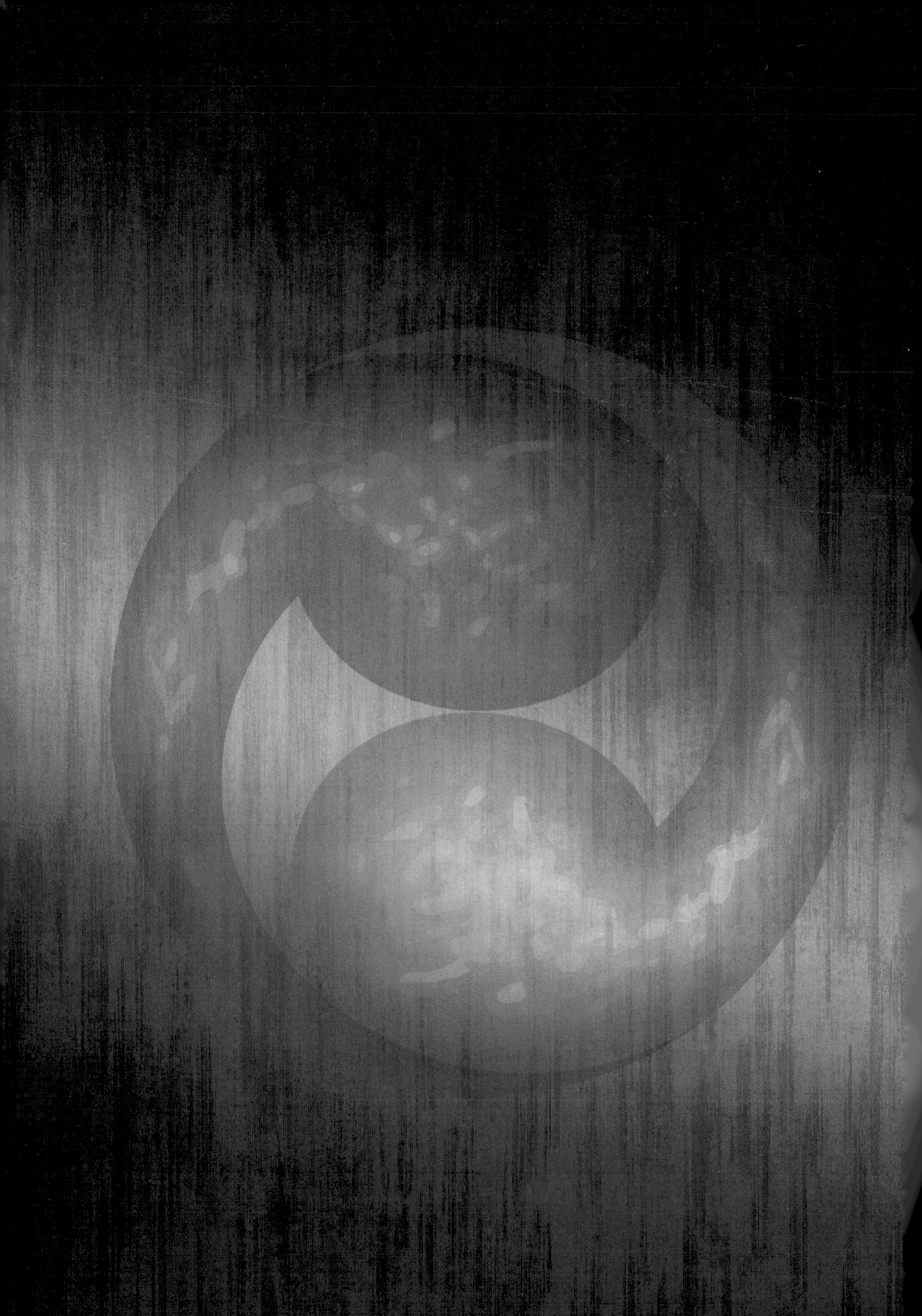

Chapter 26
by

Ron
marz
WRITER

Jim
cheung
PENCILER

Don
hillsman II
INKER

Jason
keith
COLORIST

Troy
peteri
LETTERER

All you have in this world, all you can truly depend upon, is your own two hands. My entire life has taught me that.

My name is Elijah. I am a slave. Or at least I was born one, and have known nothing else in my life. I am of the Lesser Races, and in Raven lands, slavery is the only lot the Lesser Races have ever been permitted.

But now another possibility exists. It is a dream we dared not ponder, a word we dared not whisper.

Freedom.

I grabbed my chance at it with both hands. I had toiled in the master's fields since I was old enough to walk, as did my mother and father before me. They're gone now, my father to his reward in the next life, my mother sold to another master when she became too aged to work in the fields.

There on the borderlands we were untouched by much of what transpired in the capital to the west. Bron's ascension to the throne did not change our lives in any way. The war itself between the Ravens and the Herons meant little to us.

But what was born of that war meant everything – an island of Sanctuary, a place of true freedom that would welcome my kind as free men. Or so said the rumors that spread even to my remote region.

So there were those who decided the lure of freedom was worth risking the punishments reserved for escaped slaves. Chyrizah and Kayanan, myself and Borzhoy the Elder, four of us...

...and only four. The rest of the estate slaves chose to remain shackled to the lives they knew, no matter how abhorrent, rather than have the courage to seek a new life. Who am I to judge their choices?

Our absence was discovered quickly, more quickly than even we had expected. Perhaps we had been revealed by one of our fellows seeking to curry favor with the master. It would not have been the first time such a thing had occurred.

The master was not an unusually cruel man, nor was he overly kind.

He was simply a human.

We fled through the fields separately, believing our chances would be better if we could split the attention of our pursuers.

We shared a common goal, a malfunctioning section of the far fence that let out onto the deeper forest. Stalks of wheat, a crop that had been my duty to tend and harvest, whipped at my arms and face, stinging reminders of the servitude I was so desperate to leave behind.

I fled with the master's shouts and the baying of his hounds in my ears, feeling as though my feet scarcely touched the ground beneath them.

I have never run so fast.

Borzhoy the Elder was not fast enough.

He was an old man, and well past his prime. In thinking on it now, with the clear perspective of hindsight, I wonder whether escape truly had ever been his intention. I think, perhaps, he'd always meant to give the master and his overseers an easy target to pursue, allowing the rest of us to slip away into the night. He bought us our chance at freedom with his life.

I can never repay the debt. I will never forget it.

We had arranged to meet under a great tree on the
shores of the swamp to the north. Again, it was
Borzhoy who had suggested the swamp, once having
been there himself as part of a work party. He believed
the treacherous terrain would discourage any pursuers
who still might have dogged our trail, and so it was.

Chyrizah and I had grown up together, while
Kayanan had been bought and brought to the estate.
To be thrust into such a wild place was far beyond
any of our experiences.

I had never in my life ventured beyond the estate's perimeter. Until I stepped through that fence and into the night beyond, the entirety of my world had consisted of the fields and the slave quarters, and upon occasion as a child, a venture inside the main house.

The unfamiliarity of our surroundings bred unease in us, the muffled and somehow secret sounds of the swamp only adding to it. Even the ground beneath our feet seemed insubstantial, as if threatening to draw us in and swallow us. But our fear was outweighed by the intoxication of being free, truly free, for the very first time.

A meager fire had never shed so much warmth, food scavenged from such a rotted place had never tasted so sweet, and the fellowship of others had never been so rich.

You live in a narrow world as a slave. You understand all the harms that could befall you, and you make your peace with them. You accept that state of fear because there is no other choice, and because there is a certain security to so intimately knowing the threats facing you.

We had traded the dangers we knew for a host we did not. We began to believe we could survive in this new world.

But the world has teeth.

A single night had not even
passed, and we'd lost two of our
number. I felt despair's cold hand
around my heart and heard its
voice in my head. It told me
those who had stayed behind,
those whose fear outweighed
their courage, had been the wiser,
that we were fools soon to die for
daring to hope.

I comforted Chyrizah as
best I could through that
long night, realizing
that in all the world, we
had only each other.

We pressed on. If Chyrizah harbored doubts she did not express them, and I kept my fears to myself.

We pushed north, intending to be gone from Raven lands as quickly as possible before turning west toward the sea. The land began to open to us.

I scarcely could have believed the whole of the world was so vast. The vistas before us, bathed in sunlight, showed me the world's true face was one of magnificence, not the drab countenance I had known since birth.

I never could have imagined sights so beautiful, and yet I beheld them each day. Every dawn brought a new and more spectacular panorama, and with it a bit more of despair's weight fell from my shoulders.

We stayed far from the places of men, voyaging into rugged territories with only one another for companionship. Chyrizah and I came to depend upon one another, and in turn support one another.

As our journey progressed, I came to realize that even if our venture ended in failure, if we perished before ever reaching the Sanctuary Isle, I would not have traded the experience. I had been witness to unforgettable beauty. I had known the sweet taste of freedom.

And I had known love.

More than once we were reminded of the fate from which we had escaped, a fate that so many others still shared. Worse, it was not within our power to help those who were still shackled by the chains of slavery. We could only cling to the shadows and watch the misery of others.

The capture, either dead or alive, of escaped slaves is a lucrative business. More than once we managed to avoid being taken by one hunter or another, though we owed our escapes – some far more narrow than I care to remember – as much to luck as to our own ingenuity.

I had heard tales of a Lesser Races bounty hunter who preyed upon his own kind, but I dismissed the notion. I could not bring myself to believe such a thing was possible.

The instances of danger we endured were outnumbered by those of utter peace. Avalon's panorama spread itself before us, a splendor I came to think of as an expansive reflection of the freedom we had claimed for ourselves.

We traversed the spine of the world, moving ever westward toward the coast and the Great Sea beyond.

At times I would think of those who had wrested the Tournament Isle from the kingdoms of the East and West. Two humans of royal blood, a Heron prince and a Raven princess, had turned their backs upon their lineage in order give the Lesser Races a place of freedom. True freedom, not the servitude and repression – if not actual slavery – to which our brethren in Heron lands are subjected.

Though I could not fathom why humans would choose to aid our people, I could understand the courage demanded by such an act of defiance. It is the same courage of a slave defying a master.

Many of the threats that had dogged our trail fell away as we climbed higher into the mountains. The snow-choked passes, however, held dangers all their own.

But we were not those same fearful slaves who had slunk through a broken fence and into the covering darkness. We had learned to overcome the hardships in our path, and grasped life with the tenacity of those who understand how fleeting it can be. We fought for our survival.

We killed for it.

I've no idea how many days had passed before we smelled the tang of salt in the air. Though I know it could have been no more than a few hours, it seemed an eternity before we crested a bluff and finally beheld the Great Sea. So much water, more than could ever possibly exist to the eyes of one who had never seen so much as a tarn. Its sheer, unbroken immensity, reaching as far as the eye could see and beyond, generated equal parts exhilaration and foreboding within me.

We built a boat from what could be scavenged, sometimes taking from the beach, other times traveling leagues for some necessary binding or scrap.

My hands knew the tilling of soil, not the raising of sails or tacking against the wind. How could I, whose earliest memories are of working the earth, ever hope to be a sailor? And yet, I had been born a slave, and found the strength to be something else.

Even before we escaped the estate we had taught ourselves to locate a direction by reading the stars in the night sky. It's what allowed us to stay our course west across the land. Continuing across the sea would be no different.

I was enough of a realist to know we stood a far better chance of drowning, or perishing from exposure, than we did of ever reaching our goal. But we had not come so far and sacrificed so much to stop short. We set sail and placed ourselves in the hands of providence as fair winds pushed us into the unknown. The entirety of our journey, of our attempt at grasping freedom, had been a voyage into the unknown.

Each day we searched the horizon for a telltale break in the vastness of the sea. I'd heard stories of sea creatures, once slaves themselves, who would come to the aid of mariners. If indeed they do exist, they did not present themselves to us.

We sailed on, blessed with clear skies and calm seas. At times we sailed across a surface of glass. At others we rolled with gentle swells. We rationed our fresh water stores and subsisted on what of the ocean's bounty we could catch. Neither of us had ever eaten fish, and we savored each new taste.

It was nearly idyllic.

But it didn't last.

The sea had provided for us. Now it exacted its price. The storm was not a sudden gale, blowing up without warning. That would have been far better, far kinder, than being forced to watch our doom gathering strength and knowing we could not outrun it. Instead it bruised the northern sky, white clouds darkening to gray, and gray to black.

The storm unleashed its fury upon us as if reminding us of our insignificance, smashing to tinder the boat we had so proudly crafted. The wind howled and the sea heaved and bucked like a great beast, threatening to swallow us for having the temerity to believe we could escape the lives that had been ordained for us. Chyrizah and I clung to one another, as we had since that first night.

But even the things you love slip from your grasp.

I believed I was dead.

I wished I was.

The storm had passed and left me adrift and alone, clinging to a piece of flotsam. All our efforts, all our sacrifice, had come to this cruel end. I had lost even the chance to die along with Chyrizah. I had lost everything except that which no longer held any meaning for me – my own life. And then the morning fog burned away...

...and the island appeared to me.

At first I believed it to be merely an illusion, a phantom to taunt me in my final hours.

I struck out for the shore anyway, pushing myself toward it with whatever of my strength remained. By the time I had reached the shallows and convinced myself of the island's reality, I could pull myself no further. I was resigned that the rocks of the beach would serve to mark my grave.

All you have in this world is your own two hands.

Even now, after all I have been through, I believe that to be so.

But I also have learned there is a time to reach out and grasp other hands, hands offered in help.

NEXT
MONTH
IN...

EDGE

RUSE
Chapter 10
Lightborne threatens
to level the entire city
of Parthington for the
Enigmatic Prism.

SCION
Chapter 27
A monstrous assassin
plots Ethan's demise.

SIGIL
Chapter 26
With Gaia in ruins, Sam
heads for a final assault
on the Saurian home
world.

THE FIRST
Chapter 20
Will Pyrem be the one
to save Ingra from the
many arms of Ervulsh?

WAY OF THE RAT
Chapter 3
Boon learns the significance
of the mystic artifacts he's
stolen.

MYSTIC
Chapters 25 & 26
Giselle must undergo a
series of trials to prove
she's worthy to protect
Cyress.

It's Never Too Late To Try Forge!

Route 666
High-Octane Horror
In Chapter 1 we've got everything ghouls, ghosts, and girls. It's the debut of the horror comic with the Cold War bite!
Written by Tony Bedard with art by Karl Moline, John Dell and Nick Bell.

The Path
A Samurai Epic
In Chapter 6, Obo-san wrestles his demons as Ryuichi lays siege to the monastery.
Written by Ron Marz with art by Bart Sears, Mark Pennington and Micheal Atiyeh.

Sojourn
A Sword and Sorcery Tale
In Chapter 12, Kreeg discovers creepy monsters in the forest, while Neven confronts Arwyn.
Written by Ron Marz with art by June Bringman, Drew Geraci and Jason Lambei

JUST LOOK
WHAT'S COMING IN
FORGE
#7

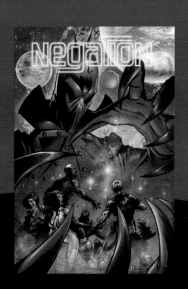

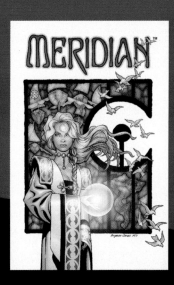

Crux
Cosmic Science Fiction
In Chapter 16, Aristophanes
and Thraxis show the Crux
team just how to take down
the Negation!
Written by Chuck Dixon
with art by Steve Epting,
Rick Magyar, and
Frank D'Armata

Negation
Escape From A Universe
In Chapters 8 & 9, the
lawbringer Oztr wails
on our team of escapees,
and Komptin gets his dog.
Written by Tony Bedard
with art by Paul Pelletier,
Dave Meikis, and
James Rochelle

Meridian
Fairy Tale Fantasy
In Chapter 27,
there's a new sheriff
in town, as Sephie
takes over Ilahn's estates.
Written by Barbara Kesel
with art by Steve McNiven,
Tom Simmons, and
Morry Hollowell

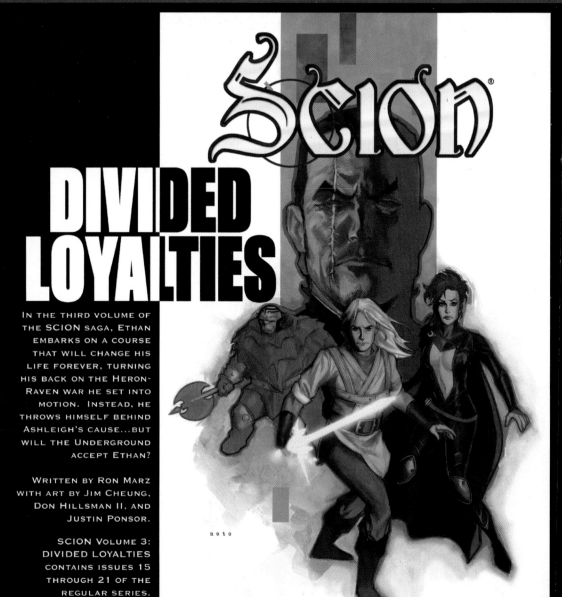

CROSSGEN COMICS

Graphic Novels

THE FIRST 1	Two Houses Divided	$19.95	1-931484-04-X
THE FIRST 2	Magnificent Tension	$19.95	1-931484-17-1
MYSTIC 1	Rite of Passage	$19.95	1-931484-00-7
MYSTIC 2	The Demon Queen	$19.95	1-931484-06-6
MYSTIC 3	Seige of Scales	$15.95	1-931484-24-4
MERIDIAN 1	Flying Solo	$19.95	1-931484-03-1
MERIDIAN 2	Going to Ground	$19.95	1-931484-09-0
MERIDIAN 3	Taking the Skies	$15.95	1-931484-21-X
SCION 1	Conflict of Conscience	$19.95	1-931484-02-3
SCION 2	Blood for Blood	$19.95	1-931484-08-2
SCION 3	Divided Loyalties	$15.95	1-931484-26-0
SIGIL 1	Mark of Power	$19.95	1-931484-01-5
SIGIL 2	The Marked Man	$19.95	1-931484-07-4
SIGIL 3	The Lizard God	$15.95	1-931484-28-7
CRUX 1	Atlantis Rising	$15.95	1-931484-14-7
NEGATION 1	Bohica	$19.95	1-931484-30-9
SOJOURN 1	From the Ashes	$19.95	1-931484-15-5
SOJOURN 2	The Dragon's Tale	$15.95	1-931484-34-1
RUSE 1	Enter the Detective	$15.95	1-931484-19-8
THE PATH 1	Crisis of Faith	$19.95	1-931484-32-5
CROSSGEN ILLUSTRATED Volume 1		$24.95	1-931484-05-8